ACTIVITIES WITH

TEN CALDECOTT MEDAL WINNERS

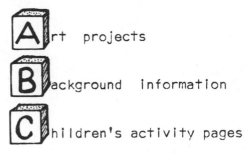

Art projects

Background information

Children's activity pages

by

Roberta Burnett
Jane E. Hahn
Virginia T. Mealy

ISBN 0-913839-06-X

Book
Lures
Inc.

P.O. Box 9450
O'Fallon, Mo.
63366

Printed in U.S.A.

Copyright 1980 by Book Lures, Inc.

TEN CALDECOTT MEDAL WINNERS

Ten books which have been awarded the Caldecott Medal have been selected. For each, this booklet includes an art project for students to do which compliments the award winning book; an activity sheet for teachers and/or librarians to copy and duplicate; and a final section which gives background information for the teacher and/or librarian about the Caldecott Medal itself and about these ten winning illustrators. Answers to activity sheets are provided at the end of the booklet.

The art projects and activity pages are arranged chronologically, based on the year the book won the award. Background information on the illustrators is arranged in alphabetical order by the illustrator's last name.

BOOKS SELECTED	YEAR AWARDED MEDAL	ILLUSTRATOR
MEI LI	1939	Thomas Handforth
ABRAHAM LINCOLN	1940	Ingri & Edgar d'Aulaire
MAKE WAY FOR DUCKLINGS	1942	Robert McCloskey
THE BIG SNOW	1949	Berta & Elmer Hader
THE EGG TREE	1951	Katherine Milhous
NINE DAYS TO CHRISTMAS	1960	Marie Hall Ets
WHERE THE WILD THINGS ARE	1964	Maurice Sendak
THE FUNNY LITTLE WOMAN	1973	Blair Lent
ASHANTI TO ZULU	1977	Leo & Diane Dillon
THE OX-CART MAN	1980	Barbara Cooney

Chinese Girl Bookmark

What you need:

I sheet of manila paper
I sheet of black construction paper
I envelope
crayons
scissors
glue

What to do:

1. Cut out a circle about 4" across from the manila paper for a head.

2. Cut out an oblong just a bit larger than the head from black paper, for hair. Fit head on top.

3. Cut 3 strips of black paper 1/4" x 5" long. Glue them together on one end.

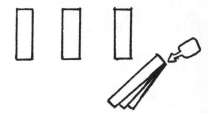

4. Braid the strips. Bend the paper as you braid. Glue the head and black hair oval together with the braid between them.

5. Cut off the end of an envelope.

6. Slip the envelope over the head. Glue only to the front of the head.

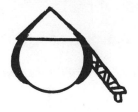

7. Give the girl eyes, nose, and a mouth.

8. The back of the hat fits the corner of a book for a bookmark.

MEI LI
Illustrated by Thomas Handforth
1939 Caldecott Medal winner

<u>Take Mei Li Home</u>

Mei Li has gone to the city. You know all the things she saw and did. Be sure she
visits each of these, BUT be sure to get her home in time to welcome the Kitchen God
at midnight.   Begin at Mei Li's home and add or subtract <u>ONLY</u> the numbers of a place
Mei Li visited.   Your final number should be the time Mei Li must be home --12, midnight.

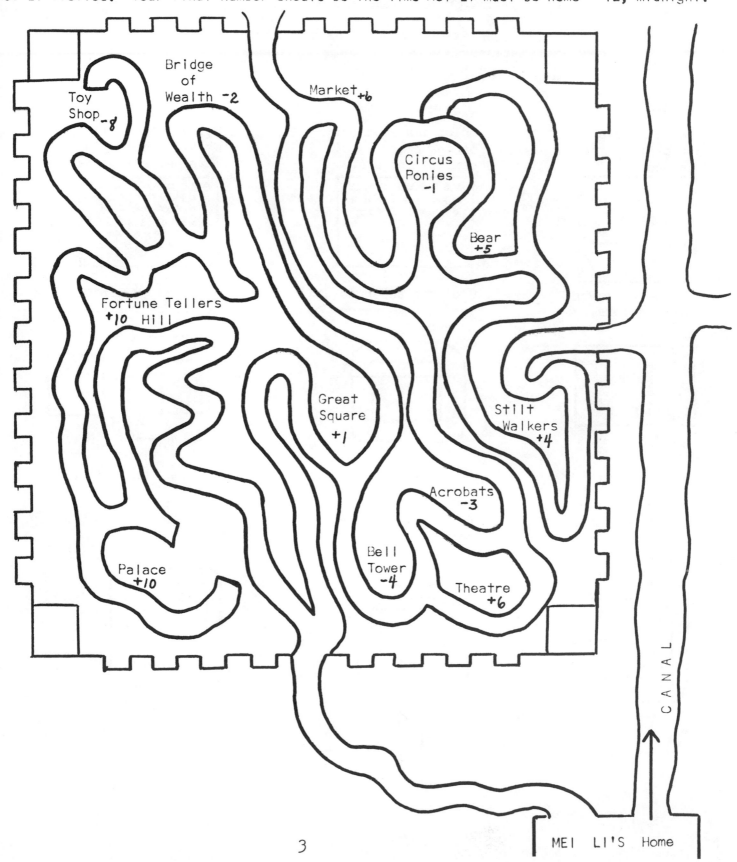

Toy Shop -8
Bridge of Wealth -2
Market +6
Circus Ponies -1
Bear +5
Fortune Tellers Hill +10
Great Square +1
Stilt Walkers +4
Acrobats -3
Palace +10
Bell Tower -4
Theatre +6
CANAL
MEI LI'S Home

3

A Hornbook

What you need:

1 piece of cardboard 8" x 10"
1 piece of paper 5" x 5"
pencil and black magic marker
yellow or gold tape
glue
clear plastic contact paper 5 1/2" x 5 1/2"
scissors
1 piece of string, approximately 6" long

What to do:

1. Cut a paddle shape from the cardboard.

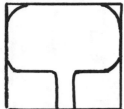

2. Print the alphabet on the paper in all capital letters.

3. Below the capitals, print it again in lower case letters.

4. Below the lower case letters, print the vowels.

5. Glue the paper on the paddle-shaped cardboard.

6. Put plastic contact on top of the paper.

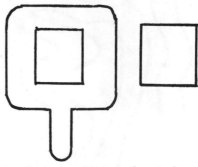

7. Put tape around the edge of the paper and plastic.

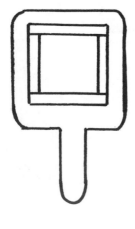

8. Put a black dot in each corner of the tape to look like a nail.

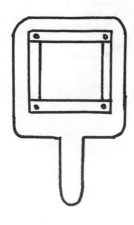

9. Put a piece of string through the handle.

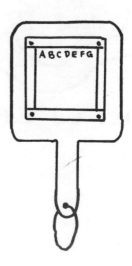

ABRAHAM LINCOLN
Illustrated by Ingri & Edgar Parin d'Aulaire
1940 Caldecott Medal winner

Finding Out About Abe Lincoln

Write the answer to each statement. Put one letter on each line. (You'll use the numbers later.) The answers can be found in the pictures of the book ABRAHAM LINCOLN.

Abe's Mother made this sometimes as a special treat

$\overline{\text{2}}\ \overline{\text{15}}\ \overline{\text{1}}\ \overline{\text{2}}\ \overline{\text{9}}\ \overline{\text{8}}\ \overline{\text{11}}\ \overline{\text{8}}\ \overline{\text{9}}\ \overline{\text{7}}\ \overline{\text{13}}$

Abe's school book, called a hornbook, looked like this

$\overline{\text{10}}\ \overline{\text{7}}\ \overline{\text{13}}\ \overline{\text{13}}\ \overline{\text{5}}\ \overline{\text{9}}$

Abe split rails with this

$\overline{\text{7}}\ \overline{\text{21}}$

Abe grew this to be more handsome looking

$\overline{\text{11}}\ \overline{\text{9}}\ \overline{\text{7}}\ \overline{\text{8}}\ \overline{\text{13}}$

Abe carried papers and bills in this

$\overline{\text{6}}\ \overline{\text{7}}\ \overline{\text{16}}$

Abe's breeches had this many straps

$\overline{\text{4}}\ \overline{\text{1}}\ \overline{\text{9}}$

Abe's Emancipation Proclamation freed these people

$\overline{\text{3}}\ \overline{\text{5}}\ \overline{\text{7}}\ \overline{\text{18}}\ \overline{\text{9}}\ \overline{\text{3}}$

Abe was born in this kind of house

$\overline{\text{5}}\ \overline{\text{4}}\ \overline{\text{2}}$

Abe's school had no chairs or desks, just

$\overline{\text{11}}\ \overline{\text{9}}\ \overline{\text{1}}\ \overline{\text{14}}\ \overline{\text{6}}\ \overline{\text{9}}\ \overline{\text{3}}$

Abe's school made bad children wear this cap

$\overline{\text{13}}\ \overline{\text{20}}\ \overline{\text{1}}\ \overline{\text{14}}\ \overline{\text{9}}$

NOW, break the code!
Under each letter that you wrote above, there is a number. Use the numbers to tell you which letters to write on these lines below. The three words will tell about Abraham Lincoln.

Abraham Lincoln was $\overline{\text{16}}\ \overline{\text{7}}\ \overline{\text{5}}\ \overline{\text{5}}$' $\overline{\text{2}}\ \overline{\text{4}}\ \overline{\text{4}}\ \overline{\text{13}}$ - $\overline{\text{1}}\ \overline{\text{7}}\ \overline{\text{16}}\ \overline{\text{20}}\ \overline{\text{8}}\ \overline{\text{9}}\ \overline{\text{13}}$' and always

$\overline{\text{6}}\ \overline{\text{4}}\ \overline{\text{1}}\ \overline{\text{9}}\ \overline{\text{3}}\ \overline{\text{16}}$.

5

Chalk Ducklings

What you need:

I piece of drawing paper
colored chalk
pencil
tissue

What to do:

1. Use your pencil to draw a duck.

2. Start on the pencil line. Use colored chalk. Draw around the duck.

3. Keep drawing lines inside the body of the duck until it is filled in.

4. Use a soft tissue. Softly blend the colors together so they look like feathers.

5. You might: put several ducklings in a row on your paper,

or

6. You can use colored chalk to make your ducks look like mallards.

MAKE WAY FOR DUCKLINGS
Illustrated by Robert McCloskey
1942 Caldecott Medal winner

Animal Puzzle

Look for some words that were in the story MAKE WAY FOR DUCKLINGS. Color in these
spaces. Leave the other spaces blank. Try to find the animal that was in the story.

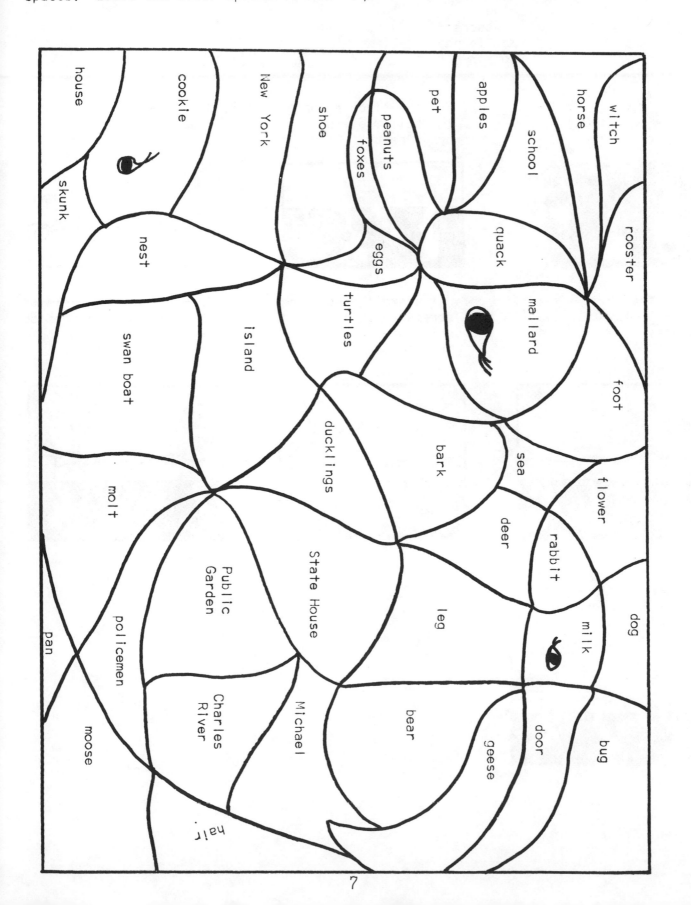

7

THE BIG SNOW
Illustrated by Berta & Elmer Hader
1949 Caldecott Medal winner

Hibernating Animals

What you need:

I piece of brown construction paper
1/2 piece of black construction paper
I strip of white construction paper, 2" x 12"
glue
scissors
manila paper
cotton

What to do:

1. Cut 4 tunnels in the black paper. Cut circles at the end.

2. Put the black paper at the bottom of the brown paper.

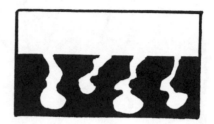

3. Cut a wavy line on one side of the white strip.

4. Glue the white strip on top of the black paper.

5. Cut a small house from scraps. Glue it on the white and draw a bare tree beside it.

6. Draw sleeping animals on the manila. Cut them out and put them at the bottom of the tunnels.

7. Use cotton to make snow on the ground, house's roof, and tree.

Animals in Winter

In the story THE BIG SNOW, we meet many, many animals who live differently in winter. From this list, can you tell which animals go where it is warmer for the winter and which animals hibernate (take long naps) during the winter?

skunks	blue birds	geese
chipmunks	groundhogs	raccoons

ANIMALS THAT FLY SOUTH   ANIMALS THAT HIBERNATE

_____   _____

_____   _____

                                           _____

                                           _____

Some animals grow warm coats, store up food, or go out in the cold to find food in winter. Use this list to fill in the spaces, one letter on each line.

pheasants	deer	blue jays
crows	sparrows	chick-a-dees

ANIMALS THAT DO NOT FLY SOUTH OR HIBERNATE

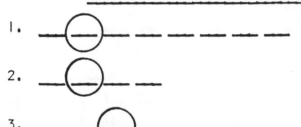

1. __Ⓞ__ __ __ __ __
2. _Ⓞ_ __ __
3. __ Ⓞ __ __ __
4. Ⓞ__ __ __ __ __
5. _Ⓞ_ __   __ __
6. __ __ __ __ -__- Ⓞ__ __

Now write the letters that are circled, in order, on the lines below. This will tell you what else these animals need to live during THE BIG SNOW.

__ __ __ __ __ __ .

MAN AND BEAST

In the story THE BIG SNOW, the man and woman try to help the animals who are in need because of the weather conditions.

During times of severe weather, animals can, and often do, help people.

List some animals which could help people during a blizzard.

_____   _____   _____   _____

List some animals which could help people during a hurricane.

_____   _____   _____   _____

Explain one way a dog could help people during a blizzard.

_____

_____

Can you think of one way in which a pigeon could help people after a hurricane?

_____

_____

Fill in the chart below by telling how a man could help an animal and then how an animal could help man during each of the times of severe weather. Tell the kind of animal and exactly what it could do or what could be done for it.

	How Man Could Help Animals	How An Animal Could Help Man
blizzard		
tornado		
monsoon		
hurricane		

Scratched Egg

What you need: manila paper
dark crayons
scissors
unbent paper clip

What to do:

1. Draw an egg shape on your paper.

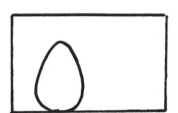

2. Cover it heavily with a dark crayon.

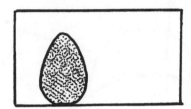

3. Use the tip of a paper clip. Scratch a design into the crayon.

4. Cut out the egg.

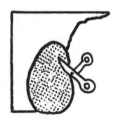

5. You might: draw several scratched eggs

and

6. Put them on a tree that you drew on another sheet of paper

7. **or**
   Put them in a basket that you drew on paper.

THE EGG TREE
Illustrated by Katherine Milhous
1951 Caldecott Medal winner

Egg Hunt

The children in the story THE EGG TREE are going on an egg hunt. Each has a basket
to gather the eggs they find. Follow their paths and tell how many eggs each child
gathers. Then tell who is the winner with the most eggs.

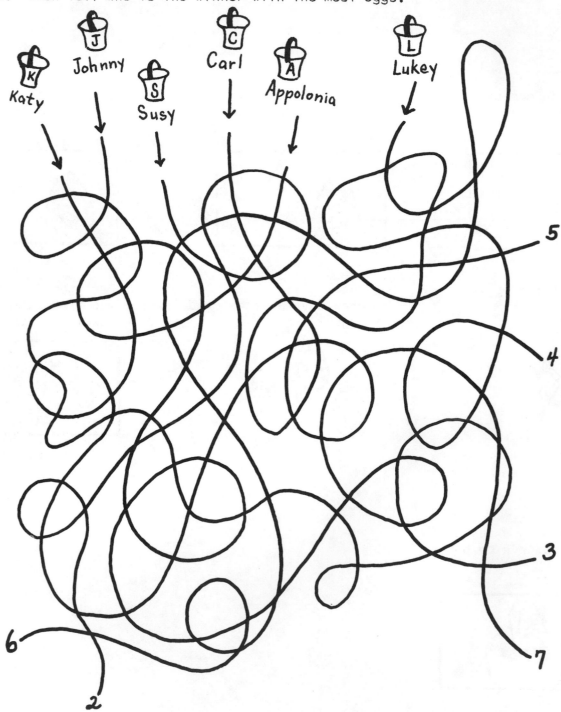

Katy gathered _____ eggs.   Susy gathered _____ eggs.

Carl gathered _____ eggs.   Lukey gathered _____ eggs.

Appolonia gathered ____ eggs.   Johnny gathered _____ eggs.

_____ had the most eggs and is the winner of this egg hunt!

Pinata   Peek

What you need:
I sheet of white paper
I sheet of red or green paper
scissors
glue
crayons

What to do:

1. Fold your colored
   paper in half and
   then in half again.

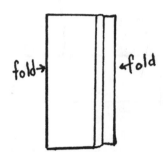

2. Make 3 2-sided
   cuts on each
   fold.

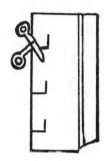

3. Open your paper.
   Fold back each cut
   to make a window.

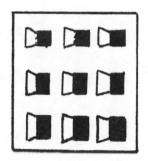

4. Glue the white
   paper under the
   colored sheet
   around the edges.

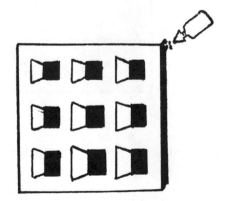

5. Open one window at
   a time. Draw and
   color one thing in
   each window that
   might be in a pinata.

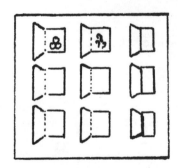

WHAT IS MADE TO BE BROKEN?

<u>3</u>   <u>1</u> <u>7</u> <u>5</u> <u>2</u> <u>4</u> <u>6</u>

If a statement is true, circle the letter in the YES space. If the statement is not true, circle the letter in the NO space.

		YES	NO
1.	A posada is a special Christmas party.	1.	p	t
2.	There are nine posadas before Christmas.	2.	a	i
3.	All people in Mexico are poor.	3.	d	a
4.	Pinatas can talk.	4.	s	t
5.	There are Dairy Queens in Mexico	5.	n	r
6.	Tortillas are corn-flour pancakes.	6.	a	y
7.	A patio is a big garden-porch.	7.	i	o

NOW, use the letters you have circled. If you have circled the correct ones, you will find the answer to the riddle when you write the letter on the line which shows its number.

Think about the story NINE DAYS TO CHRISTMAS. Can you make up a riddle of your own? Write it here. See if others can guess the answer to your riddle.

My riddle: _____

_____

Answer to my riddle: _____

Mix 'n Match Monster Book

What you need: I ditto master for each participant

What to do:

1. Divide your ditto into 3 equal parts. Mark the lines with your pencil.

2. On the top part, create a head for your monster.

3. On the middle part, create a body and arms for your monster.

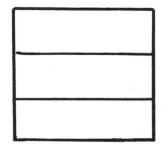

4. On the bottom part, create legs for your monster.

5. Have your teacher duplicate enough of each person's ditto for the entire group. Staple all pages together on the left.

6. Cut each page on the lines to the staples.

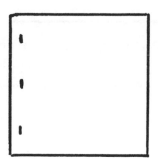
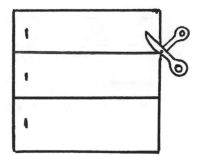

7. Now mix and match your monsters.

Mixed-Up Monsters

In the story WHERE THE WILD THINGS ARE, Max was sent to his room where he dreamed of very wild things. See if you can name some wild creatures of your own.

1. What do you get when you cross a hippopotamus with a bull?

   _____

2. What do you get when you cross a monkey with a parrot?

   _____

3. What do you get when you cross a lion with an alligator?

   _____

4. What do you get when you cross a tiger with a rhinoceros?

   _____

5. What do you get when you cross an elephant with a crane?

   _____

6. What do you get when you cross a giraffe with a crocodile?

   _____

7. What do you get when you cross a leopard with an ape?

   _____

8. What do you get when you cross an ostrich with a zebra?

   _____

In the box, draw and color
one of the wild things
you have created.

Rice   Hanging

What you need:

I piece of light-colored construction paper, 6" x 18"
I piece of burlap, 5" x 17"
yellow tempera paint
brown tempera paint
cardboard tube
puffed rice cereal
glue

What to do:

1. Using yellow paint, paint one side of the burlap.

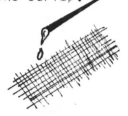

2. Put burlap paint-side down on top of construction paper.

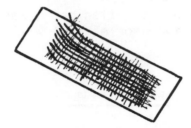

3. Roll on top of the burlap with the cardboard tube.

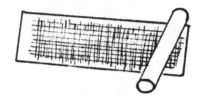

4. Check to see that the paint has come off on the construction paper.

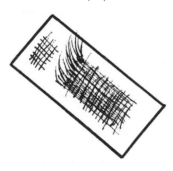

5. Take off the burlap.

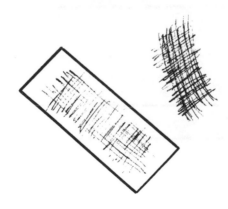

6. Use the brown paint and paint a stem and branches.

7. Put puffed rice cereal on the branches, with little glue

8. Hang your rice picture up.

THE FUNNY LITTLE WOMAN
Illustrated by Blair Lent
1973 Caldecott Medal winner

It Was Only A Dream

Did you ever have a dream where you are running and running away from something?

In the story THE FUNNY LITTLE WOMAN, the funny little woman makes dumplings. When one of the dumplings rolls off the table, the funny little woman chases it and so begins her adventure.

This story begins very much like the tale of THE GINGERBREAD BOY. When the woman makes a gingerbread boy, it jumps off the table and runs away. And so begins the chase and adventure in this story.

In our dreams events, people and places often get mixed up. Tell about a dream you have had that mixes up these two stories. It will help you to first fill in some of the chart below.

	THE FUNNY LITTLE WOMAN	THE GINGERBREAD BOY
What is made?	_____	_____
What runs away?	_____	_____
Who are the chasers?	_____	_____
	_____	_____
Who or what is met along the way?	_____	_____
	_____	_____
What happens to the chaser?	_____	_____
What happens to what is being chased?	_____	_____
Is the ending happy or sad?	_____	_____

Now use parts from both of these stories to write your own dream. Make it an adventure. Remember you are running away from something or you are chasing something!

18

Make-a-Monster

In the story THE FUNNY LITTLE WOMAN, there was a monster called the oni. Now
you can create your own monster!
 Give him special ears to hear supersonic sounds.
 Give him eyes that can rotate around his head.
 Give him a nose that can _____.
 Give him a mouth that can _____.
 Give him other special features.

19

America A - Z

What you need: I sheet white paper
                            crayons

What to do:

1. Draw curved
   lines on your
   paper to make
   26 spaces.

2. Put one letter of
   the alphabet in
   each space.

3. For each letter, draw
   one thing found in America
   beginning with that letter.

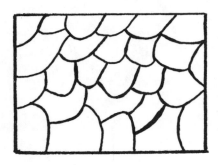
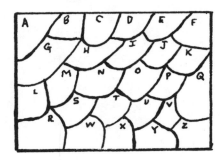
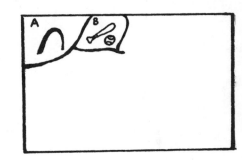

Find the 26 Tribes

The book ASHANTI TO ZULU is an alphabet of African peoples. The author tells us about twenty-six different African tribes and their customs. There are the twenty-six African peoples. Can you find them in the puzzle below? The names can be found going up and down, across, diagonally, and even backwards.

Ashanti	Fanti	Kung	Pondo	Uge	Zulu
Baule	Ga	Lozi	Quimbande	Vai	
Chagge	Hausa	Masai	Rendille	Wagenia	
Dogon	Ikoma	Ndaka	Sotho	Xhosa	
Ewe	Jie	Ouadai	Tuareg	Yoruba	

```
D A N D A K A T G A
O S H I A S A M E I
G H Z U C H A G G E
O N U Y O R U B A W
N T U A R E G P S E
Y Q L K E G O O O T
O U G E N N H N H H
T I A V D N T D X O
N M A O I U O W A F
D B A U L E S A S A
A A B U L U U G H N
S N Z D E O N E A T
U D T I Y T Z N N I
A E J A M O K I T X
H A U O U A D A I H
```

THE OX-CART MAN
Illustrated by Barbara Cooney
1980 Caldecott Medal winner

The Seasons Sponge Painting

<u>What you need:</u>

thin white paper 6" x 18"
water color paints
5 pieces of sponge about 1" square
5 clip clothespins
paintbrush

<u>What to do:</u>

1. Fold your paper in half and then in half again.

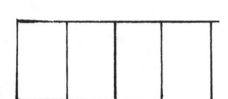

2. Wet your paper under the faucet.

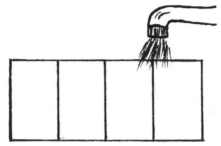

3. While your paper is wet, paint blue strips and let the paint bleed down. This will make the sky.

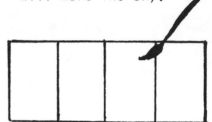

4. When your paper dries, paint a brown tree on each part.

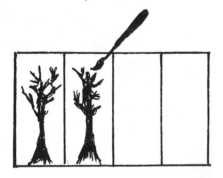

5. Make the first tree look like summer. Use the sponges clipped to clothespins to dab on the paint.

6. Make the second tree look like fall, the third tree like winter, and the last tree like spring.

End Products

In the book THE OX-CART MAN, you can see the many end products obtained by the family. Unscramble the following words to find what the end products come from. Sometimes you will find a word used more than once.

s e b e   _____

p e e s h   _____

a l m p e   e t e s r   _____(2 words)

h e s e p   _____

e e e s g   _____

l x f a   _____

r i b h c   s t e r e   _____(2 words)

e s e p h   _____

Now, use the words you've made to answer these questions.

1. Maple sugar comes from _____ _____.

2. Wool comes from _____.

3. Honey comes from _____.

4. A shawl comes from _____.

5. Linen comes from _____.

6. Brooms come from _____ _____.

7. Feathers come from _____.

8. Mittens come from _____.

23

THE CALDECOTT MEDAL

The Caldecott Medal is a prestigious award given annually by the Children's and School Librarians division of the American Library Association. The award is presented to the illustrator of the most distinguished picture book for children published during the preceding year. The artist who receives the award must be either a citizen or a resident of the United States and only American picture books for children are nominees for the award.

The medal is named for Randolph J. Caldecott, a famous nineteenth century English artist who illustrated wonderful books for children and who has been an inspiration to illustrators ever since. Frederick G. Melcher, well-known in the book world as the head of PUBLISHERS' WEEKLY, was originally the donor of this medal. Now it is donated annually by his son, Daniel Melcher.

The medal itself, designed by artist Rene Chambellan, is inscribed on one side with a scene from Randolph Caldecott's famous illustration for JOHN GILPIN'S RIDE. On the reverse side is a scene from his FOUR AND TWENTY BLACKBIRDS.

The first Caldecott Medal was presented in 1938 to Dorothy Lathrop for her illustrations in ANIMALS OF THE BIBLE. Although only one book wins the award, the selection committee recognizes the outstanding quality of other books and some are named Honor Books, meaning they were definite runners-up for the award.

TEN CALDECOTT WINNERS

Cooney

Barbara Cooney was born in Brooklyn, New York, and grew up on Long Island and in Maine. She is married to a medical doctor, Dr. C. Talbot Porter, and they have four children. During World War II, she served in the Women's Army Corps and became a second lieutenant. Aside from being a wife and mother, Barbara Cooney is a noted children's book illustrator. She majored in art history at Smith College and studied graphic art at the Art Students League in New York City.

Miss Cooney illustrated her first book in 1940; but in 1959, when she received the Caldecott Medal for her illustrations in CHANTICLEER AND THE FOX, she acknowledged that it was the pinnacle of her life as an illustrator.

Miss Cooney is extremely dedicated to her work and takes it very seriously. Drawing, she contends, is hard work, though the conception is pure pleasure. When she does a book, especially one she likes, she actually lives in it while she's illustrating it. She is extremely conscious of the time frame in which she is working and the most minute details. This is very obvious in THE OX-CART MAN, for which Miss Cooney won the Caldecott Medal for a second time in 1980.

d'Aulaires

America is the "adopted" home of the d'Aulaires. Ingri was born in Norway
and Edgar is from Switzerland. They met at art school in Paris and came to
New York City in 1929. Their award winning book, ABRAHAM LINCOLN, was born out
of a love they had to make this great American man come alive for children.

In order to accomplish their goal, the d'Aulaires felt they had to live
Abraham Lincoln's life or experience, as best they could, the type life he had.
They followed Lincoln's path, going wherever he lived and pitching their tent.
They wanted to smell the same flowers he smelled and hear the same animal sounds
he heard. Although they received many offers of hospitality along the way, these
two author-artists persisted in experiencing, as best as possible, the land and
life Abraham Lincoln knew. It is reflected in their art in this book, the 1940
Caldecott winner.

Dillons

Leo and Diane Dillon are both fine artists in their own right. They met at
the Parsons School of Design. As each was an excellent artist, they became com-
petitors, and fierce ones at that. It seemed that they were constantly trying to
out-do one another. Then, they fell in love and they were married.

Since their marriage, they have worked together as one artist. They both have
separate and individual styles, but they blend and mold them into one when working
together. Obviously, this blend continues to produce beautiful and distinctive
illustrations. The Dillons are the first couple to have won the Caldecott Medal two
years successively. They won it in 1976 for the story retold by Verna Aardema,
WHY MOSQUITOES BUZZ IN PEOPLE'S EARS, and again in 1977 for their illustrations in
Margaret Musgrove's book, ASHANTI TO ZULU: AFRICAN TRADITIONS. In their 1977 winner
a fantastic amount of research went into each picture to insure accuracy to the most
minute detail. The Dillons have tried, whenever possible, to include a family unit
(a man, a woman, a child), the living quarters, an artifact, and a local animal in
each picture. Every picture is framed with an interwoven designed at each corner.
This is based on the Kano Knot, a design used in Kano in northern Nigeria, symbolizing
endless searching.

Ets

Marie Hall Ets, a fine author and illustrator, was born in 1895. In 1960
her book, NINE DAYS TO CHRISTMAS, won the Caldecott Award.

Mrs. Ets visited Mexico and sketched many pictures there. Aurora Labastida
wanted to write a story about Mexico and a star-shaped pinata and she wanted Mrs.
Ets to do the pictures. As she could not quite get the story to hold together, Mrs.
Ets did part of the writing also and is a joint author.

While in Mexico, Mrs. Ets learned from the Mexican people themselves that they were not happy or really pleased with books written in America about Mexico. They said that most all the books showed the Mexicans as poor and as farmers or villagers. So Mrs. Ets was determined to write a Mexican story showing what life was like in a Mexican city. People there might have somewhat different style houses, but the houses did have bathrooms and bathtubs. The streets and people dressed much as Americans did and they even had Dairy Queens.

In this book, Mrs. Ets has used all real people as models, except for the child Ceci. This character she constructed in her mind because she just could not find the right child for the part.

Haders

Berta and Elmer Hader are a team who have worked very well together. Mr. Hader studied art in San Francisco and in France. Mrs. Hader studied journalism. Together they began their career by doing children's pages in magazines and this eventually led to the world of children's books.

THE BIG SNOW, for which they were awarded the Caldecott Medal in 1949, is a true story. One year, just after Christmas, it snowed and snowed. It seemed that it would never stop. The Haders knew that the birds and other animals would have a hard time surviving, so they put out food for the wild life. In this book, the picture showing the couple setting out food is actually a picture of Berta and Elmer Hader. Compared to photographs of the couple, it is a very well done self-portrait.

Handforth

Thomas Handforth was born in Tacoma, Washington, and from his early childhood had an instinctive orientation toward the East. Even before he went to kindergarten he was drawing and Chinese characters and symbols appear even in those early sketches. Mr. Handforth lived in Peking, China, for several years. He stayed in a big house which had once been owned by a wealthy Chinese mandarin. Here in the house and in the courtyard, he sketched all the sights found in the 1939 Caldecott winner, MEI LI.

Mei Li was a real girl, who as a baby had been left on a missionaries' doorstep during a famine. She was adopted by an affluent American lady and lived quite well. When the American lady had to return to the U.S. for a year, she left Mei Li in the care of the wife of a poor gardener. Here Mei Li tasted the poor life of China, but she thrived in the situation.

Mr. Handforth selected Mei Li for the starring role in his picture book. With her help, he found just exactly the correct peasant woman to sketch for her mother in the story and Mei Li was most helpful, too, in bringing in all her friends and pets to be sketched and put into the book. Even the toys with which she played are part of the book.

Lent

Blair Lent is an artist who took a long time to break into the field of illustrating children's books. He attended the Boston Museum Art School and then on a scholarship, spent a year traveling and studying in Europe. When he came back to the U.S., he worked in a department store, but eventually got a job as a creative designer for an advertising agency. Then a second scholarship allowed him to travel and study in the Soviet Union. Still, he wanted to make children's books.

Finally, in 1973, he won the Caldecott Medal for his illustrations in THE FUNNY LITTLE WOMAN. Prior to winning the distinguished award, he had three Caldecott Honor Books to his credit. These were THE WAVE, WHY THE SUN AND MOON LIVE IN THE SKY, and THE ANGRY MOON.

Blair Lent has used the pseudonym of Ernest Small at times in order to get author's credit and illustrator's credit under his own name. One book written using this pseudonym is JOHN TABOR'S RIDE.

McCloskey

Robert McCloskey is an Ohio-born author and artist. Very early in life, art was his major interest. During his senior year in high school, he won a scholarship to the Vesper George School of Art in Boston and spent three years studying there. McCloskey was rather preoccupied with grandiose ideas of art until an editor at Viking Press helped him set more realistic goals.

MAKE WAY FOR DUCKLINGS, the 1942 Caldecott winner, involves more research and study than anyone would imagine. Mr. McCloskey got the idea from a story he came across while working on a mural in Boston. With the idea in mind, he began duck drawing. First, he purchased four mallard ducks and a cage from a poultry dealer. These he kept in his studio apartment in New York, observing them and sketching them. He also researched mallard ducks at the Natural History Museum in New York and got some additional help from an ornithologist. He then made a trip back to Boston to make background sketches for the book and returned to his New York apartment with six ducklings. He closely observed and sketched them, thus showing the amount of time and work which artists spend on what may appear to be simple drawings.

Robert McCloskey was the first artist to receive the Caldecott Award a second time. He received it in 1942 for MAKE WAY FOR DUCKLINGS and in 1958 for TIME OF WONDER.

Milhous

Katherine Milhous was a Pennsylvania born artist and author. Although she was born and lived her adult life there, her school years were spent in Pitman Grove, New Jersey. Miss Milhous was of Quaker ancestry and Pennsylvania Dutch customs fascinated and intrigued her. In fact, it was a series of her Pennsylvania Dutch posters which Alice Dalgliesh, the Scribner editor, saw and from this initial contact, brought Katherine Milhous into the book world.

Miss Milhous constantly read everything she could get her hands on about the Pennsylvania Dutch. One day she saw a picture of an egg tree and immediately got excited about a book about it. As much as she tried, she could never prove (nor disprove) that the egg tree was a traditional custom of the Pennsylvania Dutch. However, she did travel to many Pennsylvania counties and did see egg trees in houses and on porches. So although the proof, in writing, that the Easter egg tree is a Pennsylvania Dutch custom is lacking, Miss Milhous' travels and research do show that egg trees did blossom in many counties in Pennsylvania.

The egg tree is a sign of the beginning of spring. In Germany, a Spring Festival is marked by village folk making a procession to the church, the young people carrying evergreen branches entwined with multi-colored ribbons, and hung with pretzels and blown, colored eggs. Alas, Miss Milhous transplants this idea into a pioneering Pennsylvania Dutch countryside where there are no churches nearby for the procession by the young. So egg trees were made for and by the children instead. Thus, her Caldecott winner, THE EGG TREE, simply tells the story of a grandmother who made an egg tree for children. Although she made no claim that it was a Pennsylvania Dutch custom, her book with its traditional Pennsylvania Dutch folk art, stirred up what she called "a tempest in an egg cup."

Sendak

Maurice Sendak was born and grew up in Brooklyn, New York, the youngest of three children. When he was about 9 years old, he began writing his own stories, illustrating them and binding them with tape and decorated covers.

During high school he got a part-time job drawing background for Mutt-and-Jeff comic books. He dearly loved fantasy, and with his earnings, purchased treasured copies of GRIMM'S FAIRY TALES and ANDERSEN'S FAIRY TALES, all beautifully illustrated. He realized around this time that what he wanted to do in life was illustrate books.

He then made portfolios of his illustrations and made the rounds of New York children's book editors. He received no work. About a year later, Sendak managed to get a job working at F.A.O. Schwarz, the famous New York toy store, doing elaborate window displays. His work was seen and admired by Leonard Weisgard, who recommended him for work. Later, the children's book buyer and the display director at F.A.O. Schwarz arranged for Ursula Nordstrom of Harper to see his work. Thus, the door to illustrating children's books was opened to him at last.

Maurice Sendak had five books as Caldecott Medal runners-up before receiving the Caldecott Medal in 1964 for WHERE THE WILD THINGS ARE. His runners-up were A VERY SPECIAL HOUSE, WHAT DO YOU SAY, DEAR?, LITTLE BEAR'S VISIT, THE MOON JUMPERS, and MR. RABBIT AND THE LOVELY PRESENT.

Mr. Sendak lives and works in New York. He has a large collection of rare children's books and a vast record library, as he finds music essentially related to art. He had a Sealyham terrier named Jennie, who appears in many of the books he illustrates. In WHERE THE WILD THINGS ARE, Jennie is the dog Max is chasing with a fork.

HONOR BOOKS

Each year the Caldecott Award is given to the most distinguished American picture book for children. This award is named for Randolph Caldecott, a most famous English illustrator of books for children.

Each year the American Library Association chooses a winner, but there are always books with outstanding illustrations which do not win. The selection committee usually names these runner-ups as Honor Books.

This year the American Library Association wants a new, and very special, emblem for all Honor Books. You have been selected to design this emblem. It will be made into a medal and given to each illustrator of an Honor Book. You are to design the front and also the back of the medal.
(HINT: You may want to study a picture of the Caldecott Medal for some ideas.)

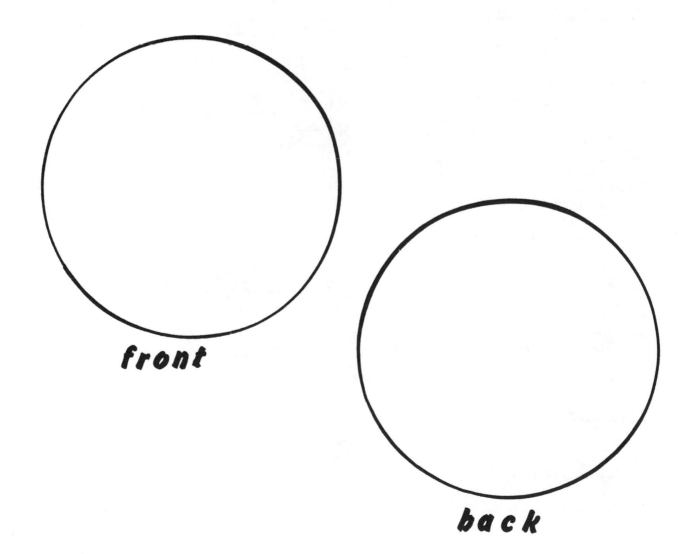

front

back

MEI LI

Total numbers on route make 12.
Mei Li does not go to theatre,
bell tower, or palace; therefore,
those numbers are not to be used.

ABRAHAM LINCOLN

gingerbread
paddle
ax
beard
hat
one
slaves
log
benches
dunce

tall, good-natured, honest

MAKE WAY FOR DUCKLINGS

A duck will appear.

THE BIG SNOW

Animals that Fly South
    blue birds
    geese
Animals that Hibernate
    skunks
    groundhogs
    raccoons
    chipmunks
Animals That Do Not Fly
    South or Hibernate
1. sparrows
2. deer
3. crows
4. pheasants
5. blue jays
6. chick-a-dees

    People

THE EGG TREE

Katy-----5 eggs
Johnny---3 eggs
Susy-----2 eggs
Carl-----4 eggs
Appolonia----7 eggs
Lukey----6 eggs

Appolonia is the winner.

NINE DAYS TO CHRISTMAS

What is made to be broken? a pinata

1. p
2. a
3. a
4. t
5. n
6. a
7. i

WHERE THE WILD THINGS ARE

Answers will vary, as will the picture
drawn by the child.

FUNNY LITTLE WOMAN

Answers will vary.

ASHANTI TO ZULU

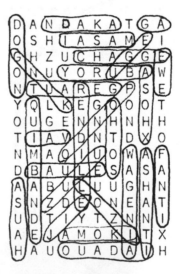

THE OX-CART MAN

bees
sheep
maple trees
sheep
geese
flax
birch trees
sheep

1. maple trees
2. sheep
3. bees
4. sheep
5. flax
6. birch trees
7. geese
8. sheep

30